PRAISE FOR:

"A GREAT SPOOF WITH GREAT ART FOR A GREAT PRICE. BOULTWOOD PROVES HIMSELF A MASTER OF TRUE PARODY." -- **EXAMINER**

"ANOTHER STELLAR PIECE FOR THE NEW TITAN COMICS IMPRINT. TAKES BOLD CHANCES WHILE REMEMBERING THE CARDINAL RULE – COMICS SHOULD BE FUN!" -- **AIN'T IT COOL NEWS**

"BOULTWOOD CLEARLY LOVES DRAWING MORRIS MINORS, PUBS AND PIPES AS MUCH AS HE DOES BULBOUS 'BOTS – A HOOT TO READ."
-- **COMIC HEROES**

"BOULTWOOD IS A BRILLIANT CARTOONIST WHO HITS YOU WITH JOKE AFTER JOKE. 8/10" -- **DEN OF GEEK**

"A REAL PAGE-TURNER, FILLED WITH MOMENTS OF GENUINE HUMOR, ALL PORTRAYED THROUGH BEAUTIFUL ILLUSTRATIONS THAT ARE CRISP, DYNAMIC AND WONDERFULLY COLORED." -- **THE UNHEARD NERD**

"PLAYS ON A LOVE OF B-MOVIES, AND IS UTTERLY HYSTERICAL. 4.5/5" -- **COMIC BOOK THERAPY**

"I STRONGLY URGE YOU NOT TO MISS IS *IT CAME!* BY DAN BOULTWOOD. BALLY GOOD COMICS, OLD CAKE!" -- **WHATCULTURE!**

"A THOROUGHLY ENJOYABLE AND FUNNY COMIC"
-- **MULTIVERSITY COMICS**

"A LAUGH-A-SECOND B-MOVIE BLAST FROM START TO FINISH, GET *IT CAME!*"
-- **THE CULT DEN**

"TITAN COMICS HAS A NEW CREATOR IN TOWN, IN THE FORM OF ARTIST EXTRAORDINAIRE, DAN BOULTWOOD!" -- **GEEKY GIRLS LOVE SCIFI**

IT CAME!
COMIC BENTO EDITION
ISBN: 9781785855153

Published by Titan Comics
A division of Titan Publishing Group Ltd.
144 Southwark St.
London
SE1 0UP

A CIP catalogue record for this title is available from the British Library.

Collects *It Came!* #1-4 originally published in single magazine form by Titan Comics

Comic Bento edition: July 2016.

10 9 8 7 6 5 4 3 2 1

Printed in China.
Titan Comics. TC1817

TITAN COMICS

EDITORS
STEVE WHITE & MARK MCKENZIE-RAY
DESIGNERS
ROB FARMER, RUSS SEAL & DAN BURA

Senior Editor Andrew James
Titan Comics Editorial Tom Williams,
Lizzie Kaye, Jessica Burton, Gabriela Houston, Amoona Saohin
Production Supervisors Jackie Flook, Maria Pearson
Production Manager Obi Onuora
Studio Manager Emma Smith
Circulation Manager Steve Tothill
Senior Press & Marketing Officer Owen Johnson
Comics Brand Manager Lucy Ripper
Marketing Manager Ricky Claydon
Commercial Manager Michelle Fairlamb
Publishing Manager Darryl Tothill
Publishing Director Chris Teather
Operations Director Leigh Baulch
Executive Director Vivian Cheung
Publisher Nick Landau

What did you think of this book? We love to hear from our readers. Please email us at:
readercomments@titanemail.com, or write to us at the above address.

To receive news, competitions, and exclusive offers online, please sign up for the
Titan Comics newsletter on our website:
www.titan-comics.com

By
DAN BOULTWOOD, Esq.

MEN!

Do you despair of your head feeling more akin to polished chrome than the thick velour she used to run her fingers through?

Fret no longer, gentlemen, help is at hand!

Simply procure yourself a tin of the new hirsute sensation sweeping the country,

'LIQUID HAIR!'

The burning means it's working!

Frogeye Sprite clattering along the highways like a tank in the Ardennes?

Give the engine a welcome tickle with a dash of:

JOHNNY FOREIGNER ENGINE OIL

You should have lubricated with 'JOHNNY FOREIGNER'

Made with real foreigners.

No self respecting
Teddy Boy
steps out onto the pier
without a packet of:

Reddy Teddy Gum

Approved by men
with sideburns the
country over.

Comes a terrifying world of mild excitement...

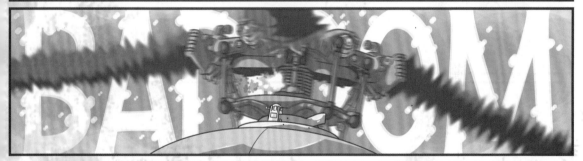

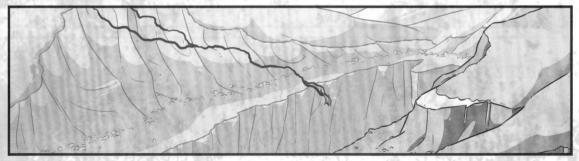

Starring:

Dick Claymore
as
Captain Mason McClure

Gilbert Forthright
as
Dr. Hans D German

Cecil Herringbone
as
Lieutenant Jock MacDonald

James Sprightly
as
Corporal Robert Lance

Sir Rutherford P Basingstoke
as
Caveman

Fanny Flaunders
as
Rose Wildbush

WHERE ARE WE?!

THE LOST VALLEY OF THE LOST

Directed by
D.Boultwood, Esq

Filmed on Location at Pinetree Studios, England MCMLVII

THRILLS!

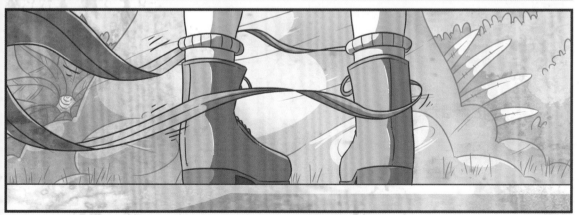

Based entirely on scientifically dubious fabricated facts.

Prepare for a paleontological adventure the likes of which the world has never seen before, or wanted to!

THE
LOST
VALLEY
OF THE
LOST

COMING TO A CINEMADROME
NEAR YOU!

AT SOME POINT!

POSSIBLY.

AND NOW
OUR
FEATURE
.PRESENTATION.

IT CAME!

SOMETHING IS COMING ROUND FOR AFTERNOON TEA...

AND IT ISN'T THE VICAR!

Directed by D.BOULTWOOD, Esq.
Filmed at PINETREE STUDIOS, ENGLAND MCMLV

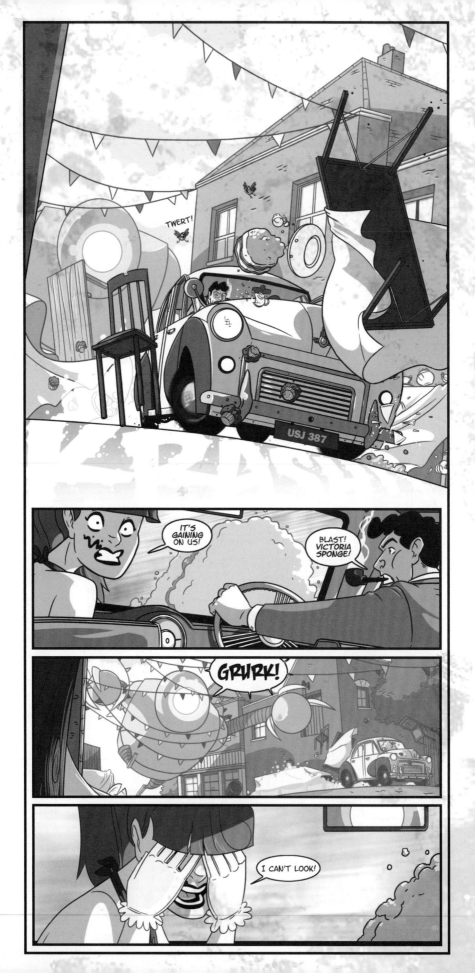

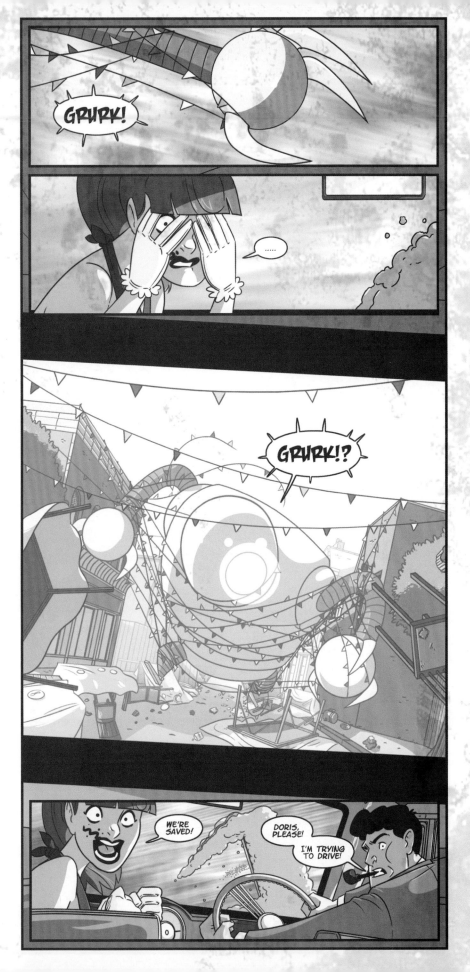

THE VILLAGE.

THIS IS WHERE WE FIRST ENCOUNTERED THE BALLY BLIGHTER.

AND YOU ASSERT IT WAS A ROBOT—

—FROM SPACE?

MORE LIKELY SOMEONE'S BEEN BUGGERING AROUND WITH A STILL!

HYAH! HYAH! HYAH!

A STILL?!

OF WHAT?! NITROGLYCERIN?!

I DON'T KNOW, IT IS AWFULLY QUIET AROUND HERE.

GIVES ME THE WILLIES.

THERE'S PROBABLY A FETE ON, OLD DARLING. COUNTRY TYPES LOVE A BIT OF BUNTING.

COULD WE PLEASE FORGET THE BUNTING?!

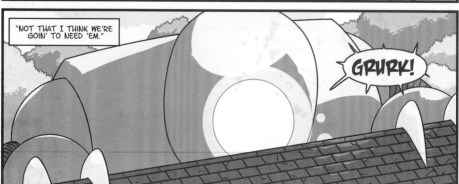

INTERMISSION

Hey Kids!
That wracking cough
means it's time to
loosen up those lungs
with a gasper,
Head to the Lobby
toot sweet
for a cyanide treat
which
can't be beat!

INTERMISSION

What's that you say?
Now don't delay!
Gin from the Lobby
will make you happy
and gay!

Consider it a
recompense.
I guarantee afterwards
this film will
make sense!

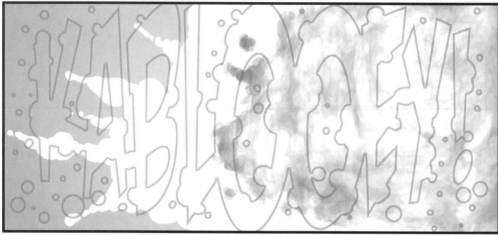

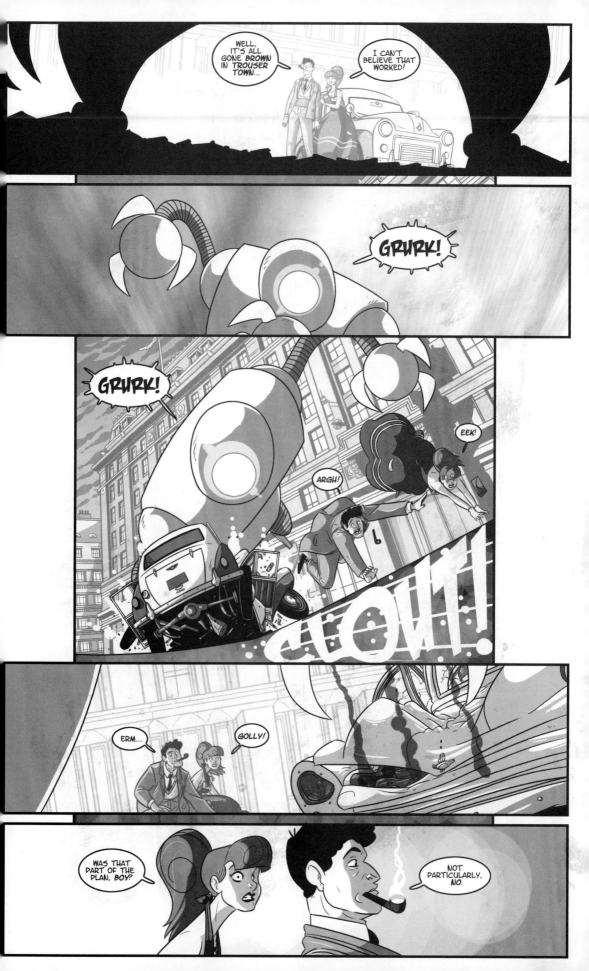

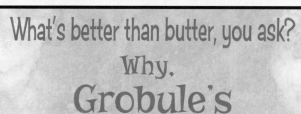

What's better than butter, you ask?

Why,
Grobule's
Better Butter
of course!

The butter for him,
and for her.

Equally at home in the Wife's baking as it is greasing the nipples of your Austin A40.

Grobule's Better Butter:
It's not as bad as it sounds.

IT CAME! #2 COVER

Directed by D.BOULTWOOD, Esq.
Filmed at PINETREE STUDIOS, ENGLAND MCMLVIII.

IT CAME!

GUSSET RENDING ANNIHILATION FROM BEYOND THE STARS!

IT CAME! #3 COVER

 Directed by D.BOULTWOOD, Esq.
Filmed at PINETREE STUDIOS, ENGLAND MCMLVIII.

IT CAME!
#4 COVER

add/change photo

Biography of
Fanny Flaunders

Date of Birth
19 December 1929, Whitechapel, London, England

Birth Name
Frances Florence Flaunders

Height
5' 7" (1.70m)

Biography

Add Resume

Quicklinks

Top Links
- biography
- by votes
- awards
- NewsRoom
- message board

Filmotgraphies
- overview
- by type
- by year
- by ratings
- by votes
- by TV series
- awards
- by genre
- by keyword

Biographical
- biography
- other works
- publicity
- photo gallery
- Twitter
- blog
- NewsRoom
- message board

External Links
- official sites
- miscellaneous
- photographs
- sound clips
- video clips

Born, Fanny entered a family with a background in theatre. Her father, Arthur Flaunders' one man show 'The Carnal Dance Of The Spoons' had been entertaining and traumatising music hall-goers throughout the interim war years up and down the East End.

Educated at school, Fanny was told acting was no career for a lady and that she should start secretarial training. Fanny defied convention and it was whilst working as a secretary at Pinetree Studios that she had her big break into celluloid as the secretary in 'A Gentleman Knocks Twice'. Fanny's roles continued with her acclaimed performance as the secretary in 'If Heels Could Kill', the secretary in 'Faster Munchausen, Faster' and as typist number three in the Hubert Award nominated 'I'll Tell You When To Stop'.

In 1957 Fanny was to start her long association with Pinetree Studios, starring alongside Dick Claymore in the sci-fi romp 'Lost Valley of the Lost' as the geologist Rose Thorn. Other titles at Pinetree include 'It Came!', 'Rocket Into Space', and what arguably holds the title of worst film ever made, 'Frogmen of Exeter'. It was around the time of the latter that stories hit the newspapers of Dick and Fanny's tempestuous affair, a matter which, later in life, Fanny has publicly blamed for her departure from cinema to the assembled horde inhabiting the retirement home she now resides in with her four 1/2 cats.

I nomination See more awards >>

Filmography

A Gentleman Knocks Twice	1956
If Heels Could Kill	1956
Faster Munchausen, Faster	1957
I'll Tell You When To Stop	1957
Lost Valley of the Lost	1957
It Came!	1958
Spiv Like You Mean It	1958
Rocket into Space	1959
An Affair With Amnesia	1960

<< (1),(2) >>

IFaS

Movies ⁻ T.V ⁻ News ⁻ Showtimes ⁻ Community ⁻ IFaSPro ⁻ Apps ⁻

add/change photo

Add Resume

Quicklinks

Top Links
- biography
- by votes
- awards
- NewsRoom
- message board

Filmographies
- overview
- by type
- by year
- by ratings
- by votes
- by TV series
- awards
- by genre
- by keyword

Biographical
- biography
- other works
- publicity
- photo gallery
- Twitter
- blog
- NewsRoom
- message board

External Links
- official sites
- miscellaneous
- photographs
- sound clips
- video clips

Biography of
Dick Claymore

Date of Birth
29 June 1920, West Hampstead, London, England

Date of Death
19(?)

Birth Name
Robert Richard Stilton

Height
6' 2" (1.87m)

Spouse
Betty Thruppeny   1955 - 1962 (sundered)

Trademark
Famous for his roles in the science fiction B-movies made by Pinetree Studios in the 1950s/60s, and his off-screen involvement with Fanny Flaunders.

Trivia
Holds record for highest number of arrests on file under drunken misdemeanor from 1957- 1959.

His film work started in 1946 as a brass polisher on 'Monkeys of Brass'.

Female leads starring opposite Dick were unable to wear nylon wigs for fear of them igniting as a result of the highly combustable amount of alcohol on his breath.

Mysteriously disappeared whilst flying his Cessna 170 over the treacherous Ipswich Triangle in 1966.

Held a fake pilots licence.

Owned a total of 7 Skot Terriers in succession, all with the name 'Scotch'.

Personal Quotes
"Work is a lot like fun for me – I don't get paid enough."

"Excuse me, are you going to finish drinking that?"

4 disqualifications See more awards >>

Filmography

Monkeys of Brass	1946
Gentlemens Convenience	1947
A Man Without Reason	1949
High Road to Margate	1949
After Anger Comes Raj	1949

<< (1),(2),(3) >>

Fanny Flaunders finds time inbetween takes to continue knitting a car cover for her Austin Nash Metropolitan.

Dick Claymore snapped just before a gruelling scene with his flask of medicinal scotch.

Anatomy of a Grurk

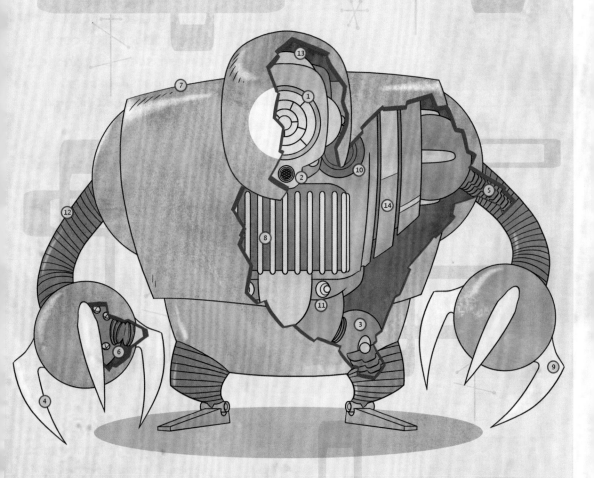

1. Radaroccutomic viewing lense with reading light.

2. Monosyllibic generator.

3. Arthritic rotoron.

4. Sharp bit.

5. Interlocking flapper rods

6. Limberon spork coupling

7. Ostentanium protective outer shell.

8. Mitigation chamber, add antifreeze every six months.

9. Clutchoneum handibles.

10. Histrionics capacitator.

11. The mind boggles.

12. Fictitaranium supple arm alloy

13. Cognative frasamatic samoflange.

14. Bovrillian inner casing

Dr. Boy Brett.

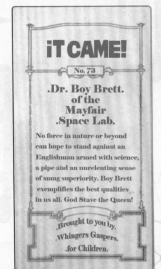

¡IT CAME!

No. 73

.Dr. Boy Brett.
of the
Mayfair
.Space Lab.

No force in nature or beyond
can hope to stand against an
Englishman armed with science,
a pipe and an unrelenting sense
of snug superiority. Boy Brett
exemplifies the best qualities
in us all. God Stave the Queen!

.Brought to you by.
.Whingers Gaspers.
.for Children.

A small selection of the popular cigarette card series issued with packets of Whingers Gaspers, Cigarettes for Children.

Ms. Doris Night.

¡IT CAME!

No. 571

.Ms. Doris Night.
.A Lady.

An English Rose from the nettle
patch of Tottenham. While not
well versed in the intricacies of
science and the like, Ms Night is
adept in the ways of knitting and
cutting the crusts off of a well
crafted cucumber sandwich.

.Brought to you by.
.Whingers Gaspers.
.for Children.

Marketed as lung capacity improvement sticks for the overweight child, the line did rather well until a nine year old boy developed emphysema whilst waiting in the queue for the tuck shop.

Originally the set comprised of 600 individual cards. Only one complete set is in existence, owned by a Mr. Harry Burkenbod, who displays his entire collection upon the surface of his Iron Lung.

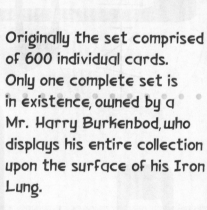

¡IT CAME!

No. 69

.The Automaton.
.Grurk.

Grurk! Grurk! Grurk!
Grurk! Grurk! Grurk!
Grurk! Grurk! Grurk!
Grurk! Grurk! Grurk!
Grurk! Grurk! Grurk!
Grurk! Grurk! Grurk!
Grurk! Grurk! Grurk!
Grurk! Grurk! Grurk!

.Brought to you by.
.Whingers Gaspers.
.for Children.

Grurk!

Braynes

FLYING SAUCER
1958 MODEL.

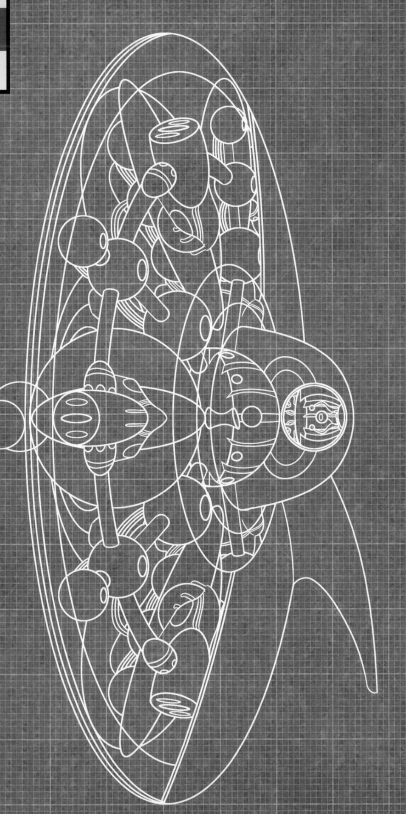

MY REPTILIAN BRIDE!

The only bouquet is DEATH!

Starring :
James Booner, Rusty Wellbeing
and introducing Petunia Feathergill
Directed By : Bergerac Cornerstone

 FILMED AT PINETREE STUDIOS, ENGLAND MCMLVI.

ROCKET INTO SPACE!
FILMED AT PINETREE STUDIOS · ENGLAND MCMLIX
Fanny .Flaunders.
Dick .Claymore.
Colin .Argyle.
Betsy .Windermere.

MYOPIC MOON MEN FROM THE MOON!

Directed by.........Peregrine Tricorner

Starring..............Edith Moribund
...............Amersham Cockburn
.................Sebastian Gently
.................Caroline Crumpet

Filmed on location at Pinetree Studios, the Moon. MCMLVIII

Visiting our fair shores and finding the bracing London air brings about a case of the black lung?

Every tortured breath induces an invigorating bout of bronchial cramps?

Never fear, Old Chum, for relief is here!

The London, Air Filtration Snood

.FOR THE WEAK OF LUNG FOREIGNER.

.Metropolitan Police Incident Report.

Date .... 29th March   Time .... 9.00 pm   Location .... The Strand Hotel

Name .... Dick Claymore

Address .... 7 Falsehood Road, Made Upton, London, LI E5
(I suspect this may be fabricated)
....

Details of Incident:

Whilst walking my beat this evening, I noticed out of the corner of my eye one red I952 MG travelling at some speed in a backwardly direction up the Strand. Thinking this amiss, I gave chase on foot, blowing my rusty whistle, but to no avail. I had started to get quite a bad stitch and my truncheon was poking me uncomfortably in the leg, so I was rather relieved when the motor car clipped a Tinker and careened through the main entrance of the Strand Hotel. By the time I had reached the wreckage, Mr. Claymore had already exited the remains of his vehicle and was clearly inebriated. My suspicions to this were aroused by the fact that he was still drinking. Mr. Claymore then very loudly and vulgarly started to dress down a plant pot which he had mistaken for the Doorman for not opening the door for him upon entering the foyer. This culminated in Mr. Claymore tripping over and hitting his eye on the side of the plant pot as he swung a right hook at it. Had I not needed a sit down to catch my breath I would have interjected far more promptly, but quite frankly, I was knackered.

One of many examples of Dick Claymore's 'eccentricities' that the studio managed to keep out of the papers at the time.
Pinetree Studio owner P.J Knockers spared no expense: this incident was reported as a Rag & Bone man's horse exploding after drinking from the Thames.

Director D.Boultwood Esq, inspects the state of the art special effect techniques employed in the making of It Came!--

Due to budget restraints, caused mainly by the fulfilling of Dick Claymore's numerous bar tabs, the lauded special effects featured in It Came! were filmed in the garden shed of one Mr Cruxley Weatherstone. Weatherstone, a giant in the field of gazebo marionation, also reprised his part of the automaton Grurk, a role he had not played since the robot's appearance as a table lamp in one of the studio's ill-fated romantic comedies several years before. Weatherstone's finished shots were of such a high calibre that director D Boultwood Esq frequently remarked how cutting them into the film made him want to drink himself to death, one presumes to escape from the excitement and heart-palpitating realism brought to life by this master of cinema.

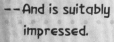

--And is suitably impressed.

DAN BOULTWOOD Esq.

A BIOGRAPHY OF
DAN BOULTWOOD Esq.

Interweaving the suave decadence of David Niven, the sartorial elegance of Wooster & Jeeves and the streetwise cunning of a pre-War cockney gangster, Dan Boultwood should have been born in 1921, in time to dodge the draft of the Second World War and become an unscrupulous spiv blackmarketeer. Instead, he was born in 1980. Too young to embrace New Romanticism, he chose to become a comic book artist instead. Mixing steampunk ethics with Studio Ghibli aesthetics, his work has graced such titles as *The Baker Street Irregulars* (with Hachette), *Hope Falls* (for Markosia) and Haggis & Quail for UK anthology comic, *The Phoenix*. *It Came!* was inspired by his love of British cinema's early attempts to emulate the crapness of American B-movie horror.

His favourite drink is gin laced with laudanum, which is reflected in his sanity and artwork.